Sam's Haircut

Story by Annette Smith
Illustrations by Pat Reynolds

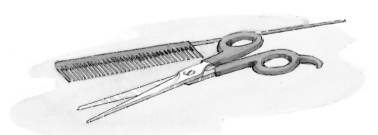

Sam patted Bingo.

"Your hair is long, Bingo," she said.

"I can't see your eyes."

Mum laughed.

"Look in the mirror, Sam," she said.

"**Your** hair is very long.

I will take you to have it cut."

After school,

Sam went with Mum

to have her hair cut.

"Hello, Sam," said the hairdresser.

"Climb up here on this big chair.

I will cut your hair for you."

Sam looked at Mum
and she looked at the hairdresser.

"I **like** long hair," said Sam.
"All the girls at school have long hair.
My new teacher has got long hair, too.
I don't want
to have my hair cut today."

The hairdresser said to Sam,
"I won't cut a lot off.

I will cut a little bit off.

Then you can see if you like it."

So Sam climbed onto the chair.

Sam sat very still
and she shut her eyes.

She did not want to look
in the mirror.

The hairdresser
started to cut Sam's hair.

Sam opened her eyes
and looked down
at the hair on the floor.

She looked
in the mirror.

And she looked over at Mum.

Then Sam's teacher came in.

"Hello, Sam," she said.
"I'm getting my hair cut today, too.
My hair is too long."

Sam smiled.

Sam said to the hairdresser,

"My hair **is** too long.

Can you cut some more off, please?"